# DANCE BACKWARDS

by Hannah Prisand

Compiled and Edited by Arin Amanda Prisand

Illustrated by Yvette Banek, Rose Mary Berlin, Dan Dunham, Nicole in den Bosch,
Laura Logan, Cheryl Mendenhall, and Hannah Prisand

*Dear Arin,*

*Thank you for making Mom's dream come true. Through your courageous life and dedication to this project, Mom's joyful and loving spirit continues to be an inspiration to others.*

*With deepest gratitude, respect and love,*
*Dad*

Includes art by Yvette Banek (pages 10, 11, 14, back cover); Rose Mary Berlin (pages 15, 16, 17, 21, 27, 35, back cover ); Dan Dunham (pages 24, 25, 34, 36, 37); Nicole in den Bosch (pages 8, 9, 22, 23, 28, 29, 30, 31); Laura Logan (pages 12, 13, 18, 19, 39); Cheryl Mendenhall (pages Cover, 6, 7, 20, 26, 32, 33, 38); Hannah Prisand (page 16).
Photographs by Sue Barr, www.suebarr.com

With special thanks to Merial Cornell, Cornell & McCarthy

Hannah Banana Foundation brightens the lives of chronically ill, hospitalized, and terminally ill patients by giving therapeutic gifts such as art supplies, toys, journals, and activity oriented books directly to patients while they are in-care.

With Hannah "Banana" Prisand's upbeat attitude, optimistic outlook, and childlike character as an inspiration, Hannah Banana Foundation aims to bring some fun to long, bleak days in the hospital.

Hannah Banana Foundation embraces positive energy and hopes that these gifts will bring smiles to those who are suffering.

Proceeds from sales of DANCE BACKWARDS will benefit the Hannah Banana Foundation.

To learn more, please visit www.HannahBananaFoundation.org

Hannah Banana Foundation's inspiration is Hannah Prisand. Her family would describe her as a creative genius. She was a poet, an artist, a comic, and a great listener. She collected wind-up toys, always won at scrabble, cooked like a gourmet, and loved music. She believed that life should be celebrated and lived it joyfully.

Hannah had cancer when she was 27 years old. She met her health challenges with grace and positive energy, never complaining. In 2008 at 58 years young, she was diagnosed with terminal cancer.

Hannah wrote DANCE BACKWARDS in 1995 when her only daughter, Arin, was in college. Arin and Hannah were the very best of friends. The poems capture Hannah's childhood memories, express her optimism and appreciation for life, and describe many of Arin and Hannah's adventures together.

Hannah wrote these poems hoping that they would encourage other parents to have open conversations and close friendships with their children. Arin has compiled and edited this anthology of her mother's work to share her mother's creative talents and to benefit the Hannah Banana Foundation.

Hannah's upbeat and unique spirit lives on in this book and through the Hannah Banana Foundation as the book and the Foundation help others smile.

*Photographs by Sue Barr*

# DANCE BACKWARDS

## Table of Contents

6

# DANCE BACKWARDS

When you're home alone and there's nothing to do
Or when it seems everybody is picking on you
And that story your friend told you was not even true
DANCE BACKWARDS

When your best friend has just moved far away
And you've called the world and no one will play
And big clouds are making the sky a horrible gray
DANCE BACKWARDS

You can't lose the feeling that nothing is right
Your head's got a headache and you've been up all night
And you and your brother have had a terrible fight
DANCE BACKWARDS

When it's too cold and dark to go outside
All you want to do is get in bed and hide
And there's no one who you could talk to or confide
DANCE BACKWARDS

When a memory fades and you can't remember a part
Of a time that you thought would always be in your heart
And you think that you're slowly falling apart
DANCE BACKWARDS

It's really quite simple, just begin with a wiggle
Before you know it, you will start to giggle
And sooner or later you're just one big jiggle
DANCE BACKWARDS

Go ahead, do it, give it a try
You'll know right away the reason why
When everything makes me want to sit down and cry, I
DANCE BACKWARDS

# Spaghetti

Hi! My name is Louie
And, I hate to eat chop suey
I see it looks real gooey
And I know it smells real phooey
But, I like to eat spaghetti
So does my sister Betty
Don't eat it 'til it's ready!
You boil it 'til it's squirmy
Just like a long thin wormy
Don't eat it when it's firmy
I love to eat spaghetti.

My mom likes to eat cheese
She puts it anywhere she please
In a sandwich, on my crackers
On big bologna and ham stackers
I would put Swiss cheese on my face,
But that's definitely the wrong place
I like cheese in my eggs instead
Then I put it on my bread

I like milk to drink
Keep it cold or it will stink
Then you pour it down the sink
Cold milk is better to drink
They say milk helps me grow,
But it doesn't really show
I seriously don't know how
It comes out of that fat cow
And cows are pretty fat
I don't want to look like that
I'll drink milk when I'm able
When I sit down at the table
With my crackers and my cheese
And my spaghetti if you please.

# CURLY

"Please mommy can't you see
The girls in school make fun of me.
They all call me curly top
No matter what I say, they won't stop.

I can't go into the schoolyard,
The boys join in and that makes it hard
To play, and laugh, or just be there
Because I have such curly hair.

Please brush it 'til it's straight.
I don't care if I get there late.
Mommy no, can't you see
If I had straight hair they'd all like me."

"Oh no! Sweetheart, that's not true.
Your hair has nothing to do with you.
It's because you've let them know
That it bothers you, don't let it show.

Laugh with them, make it fun,
Enjoy the attention of everyone
By turning the joke upside down
They will see how silly they all sound.

All the boys and girls will know
It doesn't matter how hair will grow,
There will be nothing more to pick on,
And all the teasing will be gone.

They will find something else to do
Than to laugh and pick on you,
But when the teasing moves to some other one
I hope you will not join the fun.

When there's another that they tease
Do something for me, if you please,
Remember how it must feel to them
Help turn it around and be their friend."

*Illustration by Yvette Banek*

11

# September

It was September and I was nine,
Right before the beginning of school.
My mom and I went somewhere new each year,
That was the "End of Summer Rule".

It was "our" day, just the two of us,
Off to see what we could see.
Wherever we'd go, whatever we'd do
It was a day for Mom and me.

This time we went to New York City
To explore Central Park.
We took a horse and buggy ride,
Saw the zoo and climbed Noah's Ark.

We went on swings, we slid down slides,
We slowly made our way.
The sun was bright. The air was crisp.
It was a perfect day.

Walking along Fifth Avenue,
We came to a beautiful store.
There were toys in every window,
Inside there was much more.

There were trains and dolls and games and books
Of every shape and size.
My mother said I could pick
One very special prize.

I looked and touched almost everything,
Then I saw a white cat.
Its fur was soft, its eyes were green
I said, "Oh mom, I want that!"

A tall man took it off the shelf,
And handed it to me.
It felt so real and cuddly,
As any cat could be.

My mom asked me to name my gift.
It sure was a day I'd remember.
Looking at my Mom and my new furry friend
I called my gift "September".

*Illustration by Laura Logan*

# The Closet

A closet says a lot,
What's in there and what's not.
Do you save things forever?
Would you find a tiny sweater
From the year when you were four?
Let's see….Open the door….

There are some party clothes and jeans,
Some things you've never seen,
A present that you hate,
A sweatshirt that's first rate,
Costumes from Halloween,
With shirts stuffed in between.

Things you could throw away,
Or save for another day
There are new shoes and old,
Slippers with some holes,
Sneakers three sizes too small,
You don't need some of them at all.

There's a boy down in the street
With no shoes on his feet,
A worn out shirt on his back,
And dirty rags in a garbage sack,
Maybe he could use this stuff,
You don't need it all, enough.

Try to experience the joy
Giving some of your closet to the boy.

*Illustration by Yvette Banek*

# The Red Dress

I had a cold and a temperature
So, I stayed home from school
A day to watch TV and play
This could be very cool

But, Mom said I had to go upstairs
And had to nap in bed
My choice was school or bed right now
That's what my mother said

So, up I went and laid in bed
I had a great idea
The longer I thought about it
My idea became very clear

I'll go into Mommy's closet
All her clothes are hanging there
I'll try on all her dresses and her hats
She won't really care!

So, out of bed without a sound
I moved along the hall
And giggled when I reached her room
I'm going to have a ball!

I got down on my hands and knees
And crawled along the floor
Crept into her closet, took off my clothes
And quietly shut the door.

I put on a dress of red and gold
Black shoes with very high heels
Found a hat and stockings too
So this is how "grown up" feels

I couldn't wait to see myself
I must look a perfect delight
But, I couldn't find the door because
There wasn't any light

*Illustration by Hannah Prisand and Rose Mary Berlin*

And when I finally found the door
The doorknob wouldn't budge
I tried hard, again and again
With big pushes and a nudge

There was no hope, the door was locked
And I was stuck inside
My mom would never look in here
I sat down and cried

I cried 'til I was weary
And fell asleep on the floor
I must have slept for quite a while
When my mom came through the door

"How did you get that door open?"
"How did you know I was in here?"
I gave her a kiss and a hug
Glad that she was near

I felt my head and found no hat
There were no shoes on my feet
I was in my room, on my bed
Snuggled in my sheets

"Where is the dress of red and gold?"
I almost had to scream
My mother gave me a look and said,
"You must have had a dream."

17

# The Light in the Fridge

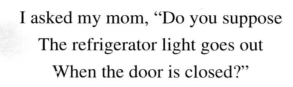

I asked my mom, "Do you suppose
The refrigerator light goes out
When the door is closed?"
She said, "What do you want to know that for?"
"Because it's always on when you open the door!"

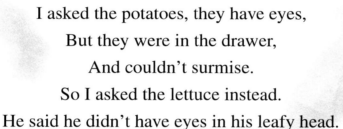

I asked the potatoes, they have eyes,
But they were in the drawer,
And couldn't surmise.
So I asked the lettuce instead.
He said he didn't have eyes in his leafy head.

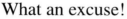

When I asked the eggs and their yokes,
They rolled around and made jokes.
Then I asked the milk and the juice.
Both said they were in their cartons.
What an excuse!

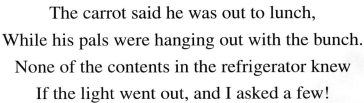

This still was a question I could not ignore.
Was the light on or off when I closed the door?
No luck with the butter or the cheese,
Neither would tell me 'cause I didn't say please.

The carrot said he was out to lunch,
While his pals were hanging out with the bunch.
None of the contents in the refrigerator knew
If the light went out, and I asked a few!

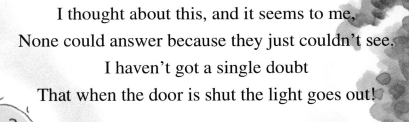

I thought about this, and it seems to me,
None could answer because they just couldn't see.
I haven't got a single doubt
That when the door is shut the light goes out!

What do you think?

# Memories

I want to live this day again
It was perfect the whole day through
Though I know I can never have it back
And days like this are few

I wish I had noticed every minute
As it was leaving me for good
Had I sensed these *special moments*
I would have understood

Now it's gone, the night has come
To visit me a while
I will have today's memories
To always help me smile

*Illustration by Cheryl Mendenhall*

# The Kite

I wish I were a beautiful kite
To grasp the wind with all my might
I'd fly right up to the sky
And touch the clouds, I'd fly so high

I would talk to all the birds
That may sound a bit absurd
But, I'm sure that I would
If I were a kite, I know I could

People on the ground would see
A colorful kite that would be me
With a sudden breeze I could soar
Swooping down to see some more

Faces looking up at me
Wishing they could be this free
The world would be a marvelous sight
If I were just a beautiful kite

*Illustration by Rose Mary Berlin*

# The Beach

I'm at the beach.
I have a pail.
I'm going to dig
And find a snail.

Why stop now?
The hole's so big.
I'll make a pool.
I love to dig!

I need some help
To make the wall.
I'll find those kids
Who took my ball.

The walls are castles
Made one by one.
My friends and I
Are having fun.

Let's wash off
All the dark wet sand.
I run into the ocean
Where I can stand.

I wave to my mom.
There's so much to do.
The sand's so white.
The sky's so blue.

The beach is my favorite
Place to be.
Come to the beach
And you'll agree!

*Illustration by Nicole in den Bosch*

# Our Box

Sure, there are great things in a toy store,

Some cost lots of money and turn out a bore.

There are beautiful toys that are carved out of wood,

While others need four people to play, or they're not any good.

The best thing that I have gotten to play

With, is a box that my mom and dad just threw away.

It came with our new refrigerator, the box was free.

It was made out of cardboard, and it was bigger than me.

So, I laid it down and climbed inside.

What a great place to play in and hide!

I called my friend Barbara, told her the box was first rate.

She came over with her crayons, ready to decorate.

Bob brought his scissors to cut out windows and doors.

Jimmy brought his Nintendo, I don't know what for.

We drew chairs and tables and things like that.

Tommy brought his pillow and on it he sat.

We played in our house box for nearly a week,

'Til the corners crumbled, and the sides started to creak.

Then finally the box just fell apart,

And the garbage men took it and just broke our hearts.

As the garbage truck left,

We let out a sigh

'cause we'll miss that old box

More than any toy we could buy.

# Letters

I love to get letters
Do you like to write?
A letter is better than
Talking all night

Words on a paper
The gifts of a pen
Where I can enjoy them
Again and again

Smiles and love
On every new line
Forever on the paper
That will always
Be mine

*Illustration by Cheryl Mendenhall*

# Together

Yellow by itself is yellow
Blue alone is Blue
They become COLORS when they're together
While keeping their own hue

An Apple is an Apple
A Peach on a plate is a Peach
When placed together on the table
They are FRUITS, within our reach

When you are at home, You are You
When I'm in my room, I am Me
But together, playing, talking, laughing and sharing
We are FRIENDS, SPECIAL FRIENDS,
You see

*Illustration by Rose Mary Berlin*                 27

# The Best Gift

The invitations went out last week.
All the kids were delighted.
The party is tomorrow,
And Adam is excited.

Adam daydreamed about his party,
And all the presents he would get.
He had figured out what some would be,
Others he didn't know yet.

The children Adam asked to the party
Had been chosen with special care.
He'd asked the ones who brought good gifts,
Though he knew that wasn't fair.

He left out little Billy Jones
Even though he was fun to be around.
Because he didn't wear the nicest clothes
And he lived in a bad part of town.

Adam was happy to be turning seven,
Although he'd rather be eight.
The party was tomorrow,
And Adam couldn't wait.

He rode the school bus wearing a grin,
Planning just how the party would run.
He'd open all the presents first,
That way he'd have the most fun.

The candy and chips were already out
As dad blew up the balloons.
The house looked perfect, the day was clear,
And the children would be here soon.

The pizza man brought the pizza at twelve
While the doorbell started to ring.
The presents were there, some large, some small,
Adam just wanted to sing.

He took all the gifts without a thank you,
Letting the children into the room.
Placing each box in a heap on the floor,
He wished they would all be there soon.

The last of the children ran up the walk
As he closed the big front door.
Adam saw Billy standing alone,
What on earth would he be there for?

His mom had begun playing a game
When Adam started to scream,
"Stop playing that game! I want to open my gifts!"
This wasn't anything like his dream.

"Well alright," Mom said, "we can open them first,
And later we'll all get to play."
Everyone rushed to the pile of gifts.
Adam yelled, "Get out of my way!"

"Move back, move back, I'm the birthday boy!
These presents are all for me.
Let me open them up one by one,
And then I'll let you all see."

The first gift was a basketball.
There was a deck of cards for *Old Maid,*
The game, *Chutes and Ladders,* and baseball cards,
For anyone ready to trade.

There was a jump rope from Peggy-Ann,
She said she would jump if he turned.
The tennis racquet was from Matt,
Who said he could play, he'd just learned.

All the children wanted to play with the toys
But Adam said, "I don't need you all here."
One by one they dropped the toys,
And backed up together in fear.

Adam leaped to his feet, stamping his foot,
"You can leave right after you eat."
Quietly the boys and girls went to the table
Silently taking their seats.

They ate very fast then they called home,
Asking their mothers to come.
Soon they left, Adam was alone,
The party was finished and done.

Adam went over his gifts, one by one,
All needed other people to play,
And he realized as he looked at the empty room,
No one would play with him today.

Adam began to ponder,
What he had gone and done.
It was he who had spoiled the party,
It was he who had ruined the fun.

The birthday boy started to cry,
Alone, except for his new toys.
When he looked outside the window,
Where there stood another lonely boy.

"Will you play with me, Billy?" Adam asked.
"I've made a lot of mistakes.
I'm really sorry for leaving you out,
Come in please and have some cake."

Billy asked, "Where are all the kids?
I see your presents, there are many.
Where are your friends, who are more important than gifts?
I notice that you don't have any."

Adam learned a lot of lessons that day
As you can see, in the end.
He found that The Best Birthday Gift of all
Was Billy, his new friend.

# Mr. Wonder

I found a penny on the street
It was old and worn and dark.
When I was rubbing off the dirt,
I saw a tiny spark.

Then I rubbed it once again,
And Mr. Wonder appeared to me.
He talked and told me stories
No one else could hear or see.

He's friends with Miss Imagine,
They travel all around.
And they told me about their journeys,
The places they have found.

We spoke a secret language
That only we could understand.
One of fun and magic,
From a distant, foreign land.

Now, when I'm alone and lonely
Mr. Wonder cheers me too.
I just polish up my penny,
That's all I have to do.

Sometimes when I can't smile,
Miss. Imagine tells me jokes.
I laugh with her for hours,
But I can't tell my folks.

Because they're my special secret,
And my private friends.
If I should talk about them,
They might not visit me again.

So, now you know my secret.
I've shared it just with you.
Tell me, do you have special friends
Who visit with you too?

# The Ice Cream Truck

The sound that signals the end of spring
When you hear the bell on the ice cream truck start to ring

I can hear the bell, can I have some money?
We're just about to have our dinner honey.
Oh, please, you don't understand,
If I don't go now, I'll miss the ice cream man.
You can go as soon as you're able
Your dad is home and dinner is on the table.
I can't eat now, this isn't fair!
The bell is getting louder, all the kids will be there.
Everybody will be in the street,
Buying their ice cream with the people they meet.
Some will run and get there just in time,
Others will be waiting to be first in line.
They will talk about what they plan to do
After buying their ice cream now that dinner is through.
If I'm not there I'll be left out
Because I won't know what the plan is about.
Please let me buy ice cream from the ice cream man,
I can still get there if I run as fast as I can.

My dad gave me a dollar and said my dinner could wait.
"Get going," he said, "I hope you're not late."

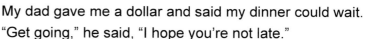

I flew down the steps and I soon saw the truck,
I could get there with a little luck.
I heard Dad say as I ran out,
"Remember, this is what summer is all about."

34                                    *Illustration by Dan Dunham*

# The Ant

Look at that ant, carrying his bread
I can't tell if he's got it on his back or his head
He moves across the sidewalk so very, very slow
Little ant, how can you see where you want to go?

Five feet away, there's a sandy mound
At the top there's a hole, the bottom is round
I watch as the tiny creature climbs up the hill
Bringing with him his heavy load with all of his will

He disappears into the top where the other ants are
Inside there are tunnels that can take him quite far
There he shares his bread with his other ant friends
I guess this is where his day's journey ends

But I wonder now, what should I do?
As I walk on the sidewalk with my
VERY BIG SHOES!

*Illustration by Rose Mary Berlin*

# A Note from Mom to J.B.  (The Procrastinator)

The garbage must go out!
Have you done your paper route?
Did you call back your friend Mike?
Have you put away your bike?
Did you clean off all the dishes,
And did you feed your fishes?
"I promise I'll do it later,"
Says **The Great Procrastinator**

Are you ready yet my dear,
Or will you be late again, I fear?
The family's ready to go.
Why are you always so slow?
We've been waiting for an hour,
And you haven't even showered.
"I'll just be a little later,"
Says **The Great Procrastinator**

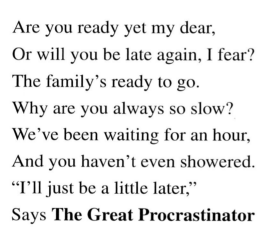

When is your homework due?
Must I always remind you?
That book report's due tomorrow.
Did you return the hat you borrowed?
You must stop doodling along,
This is very, very wrong.
"I know, I'll do it later,"
Says **The Great Procrastinator**

Have you cleaned up your room?
The guests will be here soon,
And have you walked the pet,
Or called your grandma yet?
I hope you make your bed!
What goes on inside your head?
"It will all get done later,"
Says **The Great Procrastinator**

When there isn't anymore time
Somehow, things work out fine.
He'll work late into the night.
When it's time to turn off the light,
I kiss him on the head
As he crawls into his bed.
I know there's no one greater
Than **My Little Procrastinator**

*Illustration by Dan Dunham*

# Magic

Listen
The shell is whispering
Far away sounds

I can hear the waves
From a far away shore

Feel
The spray of surf
Remember the sand

The wind in your face
The sun on your skin

Magic
Saved forever
Inside this fragile gift

*Illustration by Cheryl Mendenhall*

# The Leaf

I sit on high and flutter
With every passing breeze
Surrounded by many other
Tall and stately trees

I bloomed when the days got longer
Not long ago in the spring
When a little bird, getting stronger
Sat on my branch to sing

Now as the summer fades to fall
Many colors I will turn
Reds and yellow, I know them all
Oh, the lessons I have learned

I have sat above it all
Almost touching the sky
Seeing the changes my world has met
And never asked, "But why?"

Soon I will soar gracefully in the wind
To the place of my tree's birth
And hope someone sees my glory
As I return to the earth

*Illustration by Laura Logan*